Rob wi[illegible] the cup!

Rob and Dad went to
the football club.
Dad likes football,
and Rob likes football.

Dad runs and runs.
"Kick it Dad, kick it,"
yells Rob.

Dad likes football a lot!

But down went Dad!
Splosh!
Down went Dad
in the mud!
"Get up Dad, get up!"
yells Rob.

Dad ran and ran.
"Kick it Dad, kick it,"
yells Rob.

“Kick it Dad, kick it!”
yells Rob.
“Hit it Dad, hit it!” he yells.

Oh no!

Oh no!
Yes! Yes!

“Oh no! Oh no!” yells Dad.

Dad hops off.
His leg is bad.
Rob jumps up.
He helps his dad.
Spot jumps up to
help Dad!

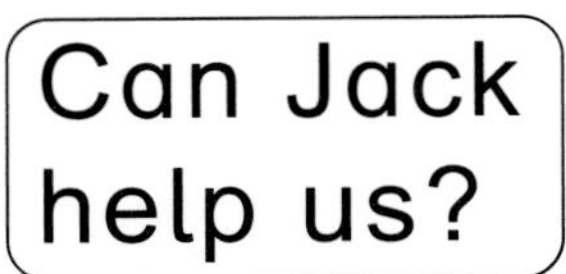

Up jumps Rob.
On runs the sub.

Rob runs and runs!
"Kick it Rob, kick it!"
yells Dad.

Rob runs and runs!
“Kick it Rob, kick it!”
yells Jack.

Spot runs.
Spot runs and runs.

Rob runs and kicks it.
"No!" yells Dad, "No!"

Rob runs and runs.

“Hit it Rob, hit it!”
yells Dad.

Rob slid.
Rob slid in the mud.

'Bang!' He hits it, and...

"It's in!" yells Dad. "It's in!"

"Yes!" yells Dad.
"Yes!" yells Jack. "It's in!"

“Yes! Yes!” yell the men.
“Rob did it! We win!
We win the cup!”